Y0-BDB-090

UNDER THE SPREADING HERESY

by Joel Wells

illustrated by Marty Murphy

THE THOMAS MORE PRESS

Copyright © 1967, 1968, 1969, 1970, 1971 by Joel Wells
All rights reserved

Published by the Thomas More Press
180 N. Wabash Avenue
Chicago, Illinois 60601

UNDER THE SPREADING HERESY

Contents

For Betty

Massacre of the Innocents
(A Trauma in One Act)

Setting: a contemporary urban Catholic home. Father, mother and their four children are just sitting down to dinner. The children range in age from six to thirteen—two boys and two girls. They are dressed in the uniforms prescribed by the parochial school which they all attend.

FATHER (*crossing himself*): Bless us O Lord in these Thy gifts which we are about to receive from Thy bounty through Christ our Lord Amen. In the name of the Father and the Son and the Holy Ghost Amen.

MOTHER (*severely*): What's the matter with you children? None of you joined in with dad or even made the sign of the cross.

(*Silence*)

FATHER: Somebody had better give us an answer—Michael?

MICHAEL (13): It's a square prayer, that's all. And nobody's said Holy Ghost for years.

FATHER: Listen, buddy, if I want to say Holy Ghost, I'll say Holy Ghost. Is that what they teach you in Catholic schools these days—to call your parents

13

square? If my grace is so bad let's hear one of you guys come up with something better.

PETER (6): Rub-a-dub-dub, thanks for the grub. Yeah God!

FATHER: My Lord, Agnes, did you hear that? What's going on over at that school? Peter, just where exactly did you learn that . . . that jingle?

PETER: In religion class—we made it up. Miss O'Malley said it was great.

FATHER: And who, for the sweet love of Mary, is Miss O'Malley?

LAURA (10): She's our Coordinator of Religious Formation and Christian Life Experience.

FATHER: Your which of what? Don't the sisters teach you religion? What about the priests?

MOTHER: I'm afraid none of the children are taught by the sisters this year, Fred. There are only two left— the principal and the music teacher. The priests spend most of the time downtown with the adopted parish or at the public high school, counseling.

SALLY (12): Only one sister now, mom. Sister Yvette left yesterday. She got a leave of absence to form her own rock group—the Novice Mistresses.

FATHER: You can't have a Catholic school with only one nun and a bunch of hippy priests. What's the good of my forking out all that tuition if it isn't a Catholic school in the first place? You can see more nuns in our department store than at the school, any day of the week.

MICHAEL: You're missing the point, dad. We're not interested in having a Catholic school with a big "c." Miss O'Malley says it's time we outgrew the ghetto mentality and learned to think of ourselves as Christian activists in the broader context of contemporary society. Commandments, dogmas and rote catechism answers don't make you a Christian, just a member of the Roman Catholic cult. At our school we're involved in creating a microcosm of future community.

FATHER: Sacred Name of Jesus, will you get that! Meet the everloving press! I've never heard such a line of patter in my life—a regular John Cameron Swayze of the dinner table. This O'Malley woman is dangerous, Agnes. Does Monsignor know what's going on in those classrooms?

PETER: What's a Swayze?

SALLY: A man who used to tie wrist watches to skis on TV in the olden days. Dad means that Michael sounds too glibly articulate to be speaking authentically.

PETER: Oh, I see.

FATHER: My God, the rot really runs deep! I never actually knew what they meant by original sin until now—it's built into them. The devil knows his business. Adam, Eve and now my four kids.

LAURA: You mean our mythical first parents? We know now that Genesis was just a convenient way of accounting for creation to pre-scientific, pre-theological people who didn't know about evolution. They were all hung up on the problem of how to account for evil in a world supposedly run by the direct will of an all-good God. So they had to personify evil in the person of the Devil and make it kind of genetically transferable in the notion of original sin.

FATHER: Jesus, Mary and Joseph! They've even gotten to you.

MOTHER: Don't swear in front of the children, Fred. I don't know what you're getting so worked up about. They still go to Communion every Sunday.

FATHER: Children? Childern? They sound more like post-graduate draft-dodgers to me. I doubt that I know any swear words they haven't heard. And I'd be interested to know what they believe about Communion. Is it still the body and blood of Christ or some kind of inner-city snack these days. What does Chairman O'Malley tell you about that?

MICHAEL: With your hostile attitude, dad, I don't see much point in attempting a serious dialogue.

SALLY: Michael's right. You're not showing any respect for us as individual members of the pilgrim church trying to find our path through the darkness of authoritarian and parental oppression.

MOTHER: Sally, I'm not at all sure what that means

but it sounds very disrespectful to me. And Michael, if you know what's good for you you'll answer your father.

MICHAEL: Well, since Vatican II, theologians have realized that the traditional concept of transubstantiation is inadequate and is turning off an awful lot of people. I mean, how far can you get by insisting that essential accidents are only appearances. We do a lot better by framing the mystery in terms of transignification. . . .

FATHER: I knew it! Another 10-syllable heresy.

MICHAEL: See mom, I told you it's no use. . . .

LAURA: What's wrong with pretending that Jesus is really in the host?

MOTHER: Laura, you know better than that.

LAURA: Yes, but I still like to pretend.

FATHER (*choking*): That does it—we're taking them out of that school tomorrow.

LAURA: Please don't do that, dad. We like it at Saint Christopher's even if such a saint never existed. And besides, we're just getting to the best part of our sex education course—Genital Anxieties and How to Handle Them.

MOTHER: Leave the table, Laura!

PETER: I thought you weren't supposed to handle. . . .

FATHER (*pushing back his chair wildly*): Not supposed to what?

MOTHER: Don't ask any more questions, Fred. Please don't ask any more questions.

The Day the
Over-Thirties
Struck Back

What was truly amazing was the ease and speed with which the word got around. No letters, no posters, no rally, no ads. Yet somehow everyone was ready for the action when the great day dawned. Here is the merest sampling of what went on.

8:40 A.M.   Arthur Manchester, 54, dean of students at Chaos State University, leaves his office accompanied by six faculty members each of whom carries a sign reading: "This Is It!" They proceed single file across the campus to the Office of Records. Entering the office, they direct the personnel to line up against the wall. They then begin to remove the contents of file drawers containing undergraduate student credit transcripts. While a growing number of students gather, they carry the transcripts outside and dump them on the sidewalk in front of the building. When the last drawer has been emptied, Dean Manchester takes a Zippo cigarette lighter from the pocket of his coat, ignites it, holds it high above his head for all to see and then, smiling broadly, tosses it into the pile of paper.

✿   ✿   ✿

9:15 A.M.   Father Edward McGillicuddy, 63, pastor of St. Irwin the Inflexible Parish, vests for Mass in the sacristy, then strides into the sanctuary where he: (1) grabs the lay lector by the scruff of his neck and ejects him from the lectern at the right of the altar; (2) unplugs the thousand watt amplifier to which the choir's electric guitars are connected; (3) closes and locks the gates of the communion rail; (4) with the help of two specially recruited middle-aged servers, strips the low table set up in front of the long unused main altar and moves it to the side; whereupon two more servers appear carrying a life-size plaster statue (depicting St. Irwin in the act of castigating the Visigoths for riding their horses into St. Peter's Basilica) which is placed on the table; (5) announces to the congreation that all females without suitably long skirts and appropriate head coverings are to leave the church forthwith; and (6), turning his back on the people of God, approaches the steps of the altar, makes the sign of the cross and in a loud, proud voice begins, "Introibo ad altare Dei . . . ."

✿   ✿   ✿

9:20 A.M. Henry Farnsworth, 66, stops his 1970 Cadillac El Dorado at the traffic light three blocks south of his home. A red MG with straight exhaust driven by Harvey Ross, 18, pulls alongside, between Mr. Farnsworth and the curb. It is not Harvey's intention to make a right turn. As he has done on at least a dozen occasions in the past, it is Harvey's plan to pull ahead of Mr. Farnsworth as he crosses the intersection, leaving a suitable amount of exhaust smoke in his face before he reaches the spot where a car is parked some distance down the next block. The light changes but Mr. Farnsworth, unbeknownst to Harvey, has been watching for the appearance of the amber light on the cross-traffic signal. He has also shifted the El Dorado into low and now depresses the accelerator to the floor. Too late Harvey realizes that Mr. Farnsworth has somehow gotten the jump on him. Harvey tries valiantly to make up for lost time. The two cars streak across the intersection. But, alas, at that point where Harvey is accustomed to pulling to the left in front of Mr. Farnsworth, causing him to brake and drop back, he now sees only a substantial portion of right rear fender. It is Harvey who is forced to brake. But Harvey is unprepared and untrained in braking in such a situation. Nonetheless his quick young reflexes take command and he manages to stop the red MG almost, but not quite, before it makes contact with the car parked in his path. Only then does Harvey see that the parked car has a red light attached to its roof. Police Officer Curtis Tandy, 46, emerges from the parked car and waves his hand in the direction of the departing El Dorado. Then, walking with all deliberate speed, ticket book seated comfortably in his hand, he approaches Harvey.

✿　✿　✿

10:15 A.M. Federal Judge Clayton Weatherspoon, 60, currently presiding over the 38th week of the trial of the Duluth Dozen, listens in the anteroom as his clerk calls for all present in the court to stand in anticipation of the judge's entrance. The defendants, following their usual custom, stand on their hands, on their chairs, on one another's shoulders—any and every way except with their two feet on the floor. Judge Weatherspoon, departing from *his* usual custom, does not mount the bench, but instead walks rapidly to the defendants' table. Pulling a large brown paper bag from beneath his robes, he solemnly presents each of the defendants with a banana.

❋   ❋   ❋

11:45 A.M.   The teachers of John Rawling's Consolidated High School move as a body to the student parking area and, breaking up into predesignated teams of two, let the air out of every tire on every car in the lot.

❋   ❋   ❋

3:30 P.M.   Chuck "Large-and-Loud" Lacey, 37, impressario of a three-hour radio program called "Scream Rock" locks the door of his sound studio from the inside and without a word of his usual snappy patter places the first of a tall stack of records on the turntable. It is the London Philharmonic's rendition of Prokofiev's "Concerto No. 1 for Piano and Orchestra."

❋   ❋   ❋

7:55 P.M.   Sheldon Fernglass, 43, father of two teenage daughters, emerges from the tool shed in his garage, slips quietly inside the back door of his house, moves through the kitchen into the hall where the eldest of his daughters is using the telephone to transmit to a friend the sound of a recording she has recently purchased. Mr. Fernglass opens the hedge clippers he has brought with him and, while his daughter screams, severs the phone cord with one snip. He then mounts the steps to the second floor, goes into his bedroom where he gathers up a book, pipe, pillow and dressing robe. He then proceeds to the bathroom, arriving there just a step ahead of his younger daughter who carries a large plastic bag filled with hair curlers. Mr. Fernglass bows, hands her the hedge clippers and goes into the bathroom, locking the door behind him.

✿   ✿   ✿

11:30 P.M.   Marjorie Hollaway, 39, mother of five, rises from the sofa and begins a tour of the eight rooms of her house. Using a flashlight she traverses stairs and bedrooms gathering up shoes, underwear, shirts, books, homework assignments, sweaters, trousers, coats— everything and anything that is not hung up or put away. Her husband turns on the outdoor lights and opens the front door for her. Together they go into the yard and distribute the various articles over lawn, hedge and bushes. Then, hand in hand, they go back inside and so to bed.

Father Custer
Takes a Stand

I GUESS some of you have been wondering when I would get around to talking about the new encyclical on birth control. Well, actually, it's not *just* about birth control. It's called *Humanae Vitae*—"Of Human Life"— and that's a big subject, a very big subject indeed. We could talk about the positive aspects of human life for a long time and not even begin to make a dent in the subject. The Pope stresses the dignity of life and the need to protect it from the insidious encroachments of materialism and hedonism and things like that. And the sanctity of marriage. There are lots of forces militating against that, you can be sure. . . .

Now the Bishop has asked that we all read this encyclical and form our consciences accordingly. You all heard Monsignor Doughty read the Bishop's letter last week. Well the Bishop also sent word that there was to be a sermon preached on the subject today in every parish and I guess this is it. It's a shame that Monsignor Doughty couldn't give it himself, being the pastor and all. But as you all . . . well, I mean . . . he's under the weather again.

Some of you have called to say that you weren't altogether happy with the encyclical or with the Bishop's letter. But then some others called to say that it was about time and where did I think it left me after all my talk. . . . It seems I've taken on a sort of liberal image around here which isn't altogether justified in spite of some of the things I've preached about in the past . . . family limitation and celibacy. But I don't think I was ever really *for* birth control. I believed in what the Council called "responsible parenthood" and that in some circumstances this might work itself down to limiting—for serious reasons, of course, that's always understood—to limiting the number of children in a family. And then, of course, some people claim that rhythm didn't work very well for them and asked me if it wouldn't be all right if they took the pill for a while.

Well, as you may recall, there was a lot of talk about freedom of conscience then—right after the Council, I mean—and I may have gotten a little carried away and told a few people that it *seemed* to me that it *might* be a matter for them to decide individually, with the advice of their doctor, of course. But I want to make it perfectly clear that I never went around telling people that they should use the pill. You've got to remember that there was—there seemed to be—some question of doubt then. The theologians talked a lot about that; practically every magazine and paper carried articles to that effect—that there was doubt and while there was doubt people were free to follow their own consciences. Why, some of those same theologians still seem to think that there's considerable room . . . some leeway . . . but. . . .

The thing is that the Pope has spoken now and the Bishop has spoken and Monsignor Doughty has spoken and . . . well, then there's the natural law as plain as the nose on your face and tradition besides that. It's not infallible, though. Even Rome admits . . . I mean, very few things we believe as Catholics have actually been pronounced *ex cathedra,* 100 percent infallible. But we believe them just the same, don't we? It would certainly take somebody with a great deal of pride to set themselves up as knowing more than the Pope, the Holy Father, especially in matters of faith and morals. You'd have to be awfully sure of yourself to do a thing like that. Not many people would dream of doing such a thing . . . well there was Martin Luther—people like that.

And you can be sure that the Holy Father didn't just sit down and dash this encyclical off. No. He agonized over the question for years and if you'll go to the trouble to read *Humanae Vitae* for yourselves and not go by what *Time* magazine and some of these progressive . . . radical . . . Catholic papers tell you you should be thinking about it—if you do that, you'll be able to see that the Holy Father went into every conceivable . . . I mean imaginable . . . aspect of it. He wasn't writing it just to spoil everybody's fun . . . I mean the joys of exercising your conjugal rights. Which is what some of these secular and radical papers would have you believe.

No. It would have been a lot easier for the Pope . . . the Holy Father to give in to all this popular pressure. But it's not his job to win popularity contests. He looked at all the facts and prayed over them and made his decision. He shut himself off from the world . . . well, not in that sense exactly. He felt it was too big . . . too complex . . . too delicate a problem to be dealt with effectively by the Vatican Council. There were hundreds of bishops there, speaking all sorts of languages and it would have taken them forever to arrive at a consensus. Then he set up a special commission composed of experts—doctors, theologians, Cardinals, even lay people—to study the question and give him their *opinion*. Even they couldn't reach a unanimous decision, some of them anyway . . . I mean a majority is not unanimity, not by a long shot. So it was left to the Holy Father to decide and he did.

Well, that's about all. I guess it's pretty clear where I stand. I know that most of you will take this in your stride. It's never been easy to be a Catholic. Nobody ever told us it would be easy, did they? But if there are still some who find it hard to accept . . . nobody expects you to take this lying down . . . er . . . but don't do anything rash. It can all be worked out with your confessor. Nobody's going to consign you to the fire and brimstone. Come to me and we'll talk it over in private. It would be better if you came to me, I mean. Monsignor Doughty doesn't hear many confessions these days anyway because what with the overcrowding of the school and all he doesn't have much time . . . anyway it would be best if you saw me. I mean I didn't expect this any more than . . . there's a faint possiblity that . . . of . . . but it really . . . oh, well. . . . Amen.

I Am a Married Catholic, I Want to Be a Priest

BECAUSE they have never really understood me or my innermost needs, what I am about to write may be resented somewhat by my wife and five children. They may find it difficult to believe that I am not motivated by spite or selfishness, but by the deepest anguish and utterly open-hearted love. But I am through with hypocrisy and sham. The truth is that I am tired of being married, tired of being a father, and that I want desperately to become a priest.

But my desperation means nothing to society or the Church. I am caught in an age-old trap from which there is no escape. At thirty-seven I am hopelessly cut off from any hope of ever realizing my ambition. The Church will never know what it's missing—the great building drives I might have pushed over the top, the stirring homilies I might have preached, the brilliant light and wisdom I might have shed on these troubled times—all of me wasted, turned back in on myself, poured back down the drain of my own enormous potential.

My heart sinks when I think how many times single people have approached me hoping for an open and positive response to their tortured pleas to join them in a game of poker, golf, tennis, or simply a convivial after-work beer, only to be turned heartlessly aside by the only answer I can give—the only answer the system allows me to make: "Sorry, the wife's expecting me." How many times have these hands of mine which yearn to hold chalice and breviary instead been immersed in dish water or the icy depths of a clogged toilet bowl.

I could go on and on with such questions but I don't want to break your heart. Nor do I fancy that I am the only man trapped by the system. I am confident that I speak for thousands of married Catholic men whose tongues are muted by conformity and fear of "the little woman." Let me tell you the brutal truth about our lot.

Our days are spent in an endless and humiliating scramble for the dollars necessary to feed, clothe, house, educate and entertain the great brood of children we have spawned. Our evenings are consumed as a sacrifice to the insatiable maw of "close family relationships" of an intensely "I-Thou" nature such as bickering, helping with homework, taking out the garbage and paying bills.

Our much envied suburban weekends are twaddled away fixing broken windows and bikes, cutting grass, washing the rusty, rattle-ridden station wagon, and applying Band-Aids to filthy juvenile extremities while our wives rush forth on wanton shopping sprees for such luxuries as roach powder, Sani-Flush, hair spray and Lavoris (my toothpaste bill alone would keep a celibate in liquor—good liquor—for a year). While the children amuse themselves disjointing the plumbing, the repairmen come and go in sports cars paid for by the conspiratorial malfunctioning of the many ingenious appliances needed to run up my electric bill to a suitably stagger- ing monthly total.

When my wife finally returns because her charge cards have overheated, and the children have devoured fourteen hamburgers, been hosed down and bullied off to bed, we settle down for the legendary moment known as "domestic bliss." This consists of watching the late- show on our pre-Edison model television set while in- dulging ourselves shamelessly with a six-pack of beer purchased in lieu of the new necktie I need. All of which is prelude to that which, for which, on account of which this whole banal life-drama is enacted—the sacred mystery of conjugal sex. Being a Catholic, of course, the unspeakable joys of this union are somewhat dimmed by the ever-present fear that my wife, whom nature has seemingly endowed with the ability to get pregnant simply by walking through a field of poppies, may conceive yet another proof and tribute to the pri- mary end of marriage.

You will understand, then, why I yearn for the digni- fied, calm, and infinitely rewarding life of a priest. In addition to the spiritual stature which is automatically conferred, I yearn for those quiet evenings in the rec- tory, those golden hours spent in the confessional guid- ing and uplifting the lives of people like myself. And if, perchance, a problem or doubt should cloud the sky of priestly tranquillity, it is only necessary to turn to the wise and kindly pastor for help and warm, paternal counsel.

Not for the priest the eternal and frenetic quest for

dollars; not for him the soul-shrinking breakfast full of sound, fury and flying cereal. Rather, he can take comfort in the mature delights of evening walks about the parish, of stimulating conversations with his fellow priests, of a weekly round of golf, of winter vacations to Florida, of an occasional commendation from the Bishop—these are but a few of the things a priest can count on, the very things I yearn for and will never know.

There will be those, I suppose, who will mistake my anguish for envy. There will be those, too, who will say that I have oversimplified and exaggerated my case in order to make my point. It is always thus when a man dares to lay bare his soul. I can only hope and pray that the Church will heed my honest searching, and move to relax its rigid, authoritarian stance before it's too late. To insist that I—and the thousands for whom I speak— take the consequences of my vocational decision smacks of monolithic totalitarianism and cries out to heaven for redress.

If something isn't done and done quickly, I may be forced—against all my inclinations—to bring my case before the wider forum of the American people. In the few pitiful moments I have managed to snatch for myself in the past year I have been working on a book called *A Modern Layman Looks at His Outdated Marriage*—and it's a lulu, I can tell you that.

Chicago and Miami and Beyond

(N*rm*n M**l*r Covers Genesis)

AS NO reader of the mass media can possibly fail to know, your reporter is paid to experience things for them. He is no stranger to raw feeling, to naked sensations that would simmer their WASP hearts in adrenalin. As these same magazine readers could not help but discover in those several golden years when the reporter's pugilistically Edwardian face peered accusingly at them in half-rolled distortion beneath the eagle on their mailboxes, he was indeed the archangel of all American experience. The reporter got out, and around and into life while they stayed safely at home, risking no distance so great that they might be picked off by one of fate's sudden left-handed throws toward the television set or the frost-free refrigerator.

They left it to the reporter to march for them, to campaign up and down the dangerous midnight streets of Gotham City while law and order took a shower in Scarsdale; left it to him to punch the bully in the mouth, to love and howl, talk and write about it all for them. They would try their own hand at drinking, but never joyfully as did the reporter, who knew how to pour it straight from the bottle without measuring it in the jigger of guilt. My God, he even had to stop smoking for them!

All this simply by way of establishing that gut reactions were mother's milk for the reporter. The reader will appreciate, then, that when he says the *greatest* experience he ever had was simply coming into being on that day without hours when God, or Howard Hughes, or somebody with considerable technical know-how, created the universe—when *he* says it was something else, we're not talking about the gaspy sort of little thrill that *you* get on the morning you discover that the $3.98 bag of Scott's really has killed off the dandelions.

Orgasmic awareness first of all; something palely akin to being socket, bulb and red-hot filament in a lamp switched on in an unknown room; or perhaps being John Updike. There was the whole unblinking show— sun, moon, stars and earth where but the second before there had been nothing, or at least no writer with the awareness to appreciate them. Your reporter readily admits it: he was impressed, impressed to the point of vertigo.

For a star-struck instant, he would confess to a political running-mate late one night many years afterwards, he felt that perhaps, just perhaps, it was he that was making it all happen. To which the running-mate, with theological astuteness not frequently exercised, replied that it was just possible the reporter had committed original sin. Subsequent events turning out the way they have, the reporter was just as happy not to have to take credit for them.

What had happened, in fact, was that the reporter's ego had come into being simultaneously with the out-flooding of his primeval awareness, and the mildly dizzying effect he had experienced was simply a consequence of this giant force rushing out to fill the limits of the void. And there were limits, he was quick to sense. For one thing, his awareness, preternatural as it was (and is and always shall be, words without end), nonetheless seemed compelled toward that single planet which Richard Milhous Nixon was later, on a droll little signpost planted in the surface of the moon, to so happily call Earth. Things were happening down there and apparently nowhere else. The reporter's nascent eye, which so many angels were to assure him resembled the luminous blue of the planet's then still surging waters, was quick to spot the action.

Evolution played its hand with agonizing slowness, pondering the simplest move like Adlai Stevenson deciding whether or not to run. Things began to stir about in the oceans and presently, in a variety of unsavory forms, to emerge and crawl about the land. Endless and bloody thrashings later there came mammals, sex, and finally a pair of naked hippies—flower children making love in the shade of giant ferns—who actually seemed to be having sensations for themselves.

The reporter, never one to beat a dead myth, sensed that his job was done and went out for a richly deserved drink. Things were on the right track and nothing could go wrong. While he was out of course, the hippies took some bad advice and blew the whole thing.

The rest is history—inexorable folly pursuing the

Bitch Goddess down the centuries only to end up pant-
ing and ankle deep in the filth of the barnyard of the
present.

Still, the reporter took understandable pride in the
knowledge that it was he who had been singled out to
cover the story. He couldn't, for all his carefully culti-
vated lack of hubris, quibble with the choice. His was,
after all, the most versatile and pulsing pen in all the
West (to tell but half the truth). He should have been
warned—should have taken some lesson from the car-
nage of the great lizards, from the wanton twinkling of
the painted toenails of the Bitch Goddess herself. In
that other extant report of creation, the strictly hearsay
account pieced together by desk-men from various wire-
service accounts, he recalled, too late, a stuffy aphorism
to the effect that "pride goeth before the fall."

It had not been his alone. The cosmos, like a sneaky
TV network, lacked the basic faith to trust the event to
one well-focussed and articulate pair of camera eyes.
The reader, who by this time may be glancing nervously
at his watch, is asked to imagine only one more thing:
the reporter's trauma when he learned, purely by
chance and an anonymous phone call, that somewhere
else, on some teak-paneled, red-carpeted cloud nine,
Buckley and Vidal had been providing a running com-
mentary of the same event.

Our Parish Council Meets

Minutes of the first meeting of the Parish Council
of Saint Prometheus Church

Convened at 7:45 p.m. in the newly dedicated Parish Council Assembly Room in the school basement (formerly Brownies and paper drive storage). All officers of the executive committee, members-at-large, designated and honorary members were present with the exception of Mrs. Ronald Birkhoff (Liturgical Committee) whose husband called to say that she had dislocated her hip at a Folk Mass.

Dr. Clive Barnes, president, called upon Msgr. George McMann (Honorary Member) to give the opening prayer. Mr. Leslie Porash (Christian Unity Committee) asked if it wouldn't be better if the Council said the prayer as a body. Dr. Barnes told Mr. Porash to sit down and shut up. Msgr. McMann said a prayer to the Holy Spirit followed by an ejaculation to the Little Flower. Mr. Porash said he didn't think the Council should pray to the patron of docility. Dr. Barnes told Mr. Porash to shut up again. Msgr. McMann said, no, it was all right, and that members of the Council should feel free to speak their minds. Mr. Porash was probably right, he said, and it would be better if the Council prayed as a body in the future, provided they all knew the words, which he doubted. Dr. Barnes said that Msgr. had prepared a few remarks which he would like to read into the minutes. Mr. Porash said something which the recording secretary (me) missed. Msgr. McMann then read the following statement:

I have carried the load here at St. P's for thirty-three years now, and nobody can say that I've ever dragged my feet about making changes of any kind. I want to go on record as being 100 percent behind this parish council which is called for in the documents of Vatican II. We were the first parish in this part of town to get our altar turned around and while we're not the first parish to get our council on the tracks, we're not the last, by any means. So I'm just here to say that I welcome this opportunity to discuss things with you in an open, constructive way. But at the same time I've got to deal with the real nuts and bolts problems of keeping this big plant of ours humming. You make suggestions and go home, but your priests stay right here on the job twenty-four hours a day. As I said, I'm open to any reasonable suggestions, but I'd be letting you down and I'd be letting the bishop down if I wasted my time trying to implement every half-baked idea that came along. The Vatican Council made it clear that we're all laboring in the same vineyard, but a lot of people have taken that to mean that anybody is free to pick where he pleases. Well, Our Lord had something to say about that a long time before the Vatican Council. You all know the parable about the late-comers getting paid as much as the workers who had borne the heat of the day. Our Lord was upholding the management's right to ultimate authority there in no uncertain terms. Now I don't want you to defer to me just because I'm a priest of God and a Chamberlain to the Holy Father himself, but I do want you to remember that I'm your pastor. Now pastor means shepherd and a good shepherd has got to look out for the best interests of all his sheep. He can't think of only a few of them. That's about it. I want you to think of me as your shepherd and I'm here to tell you that this is one shepherd who's always willing to listen to his sheep.

Msgr. said that this concluded his remarks about policy and if anyone had any questions about it or anything else would they please make it snappy as he had an important appointment with a contractor back at the rectory and would like to see the meeting adjourned by 8:15.

Mrs. Darcy (Education Committee) asked what it was that the Msgr. was going to talk to the contractor about as she wasn't about to authorize any building funds until the school library got a decent budget.

Dr. Barnes told Mrs. Darcy that it wasn't any of her business what the Msgr. talked to the contractor about and that she was only a designated member of the Council so she needn't think she was going to try and run the parish like she tried to run everybody else's business. Mrs. Darcy told Dr. Barnes that he ought to stick to what he knew best which was overcharging people for sloppy fillings and that she had every right to question the Msgr. The parish's money belonged to the People of God, she said, and even if she was just a designated member of the Council, she was still a full-fledged People of God.

Msgr. said that he was afraid that Mrs. Darcy hadn't
paid much attention to his opening remarks. Questions
like hers were obviously not in the spirit of Vatican II,
he said, and she might do well to go home and read the
Vatican documents and meditate on their meaning before she popped off to people.

Mrs. Darcy said that if that was the high-handed attitude he was going to take he'd better not look for much
in the collection basket from the Darcy family to which
Msgr. replied that he was glad she'd warned him or he
would never have noticed the difference.

Mrs. Darcy left the meeting.

Dr. Barnes asked if there were any other questions before adjournment.

Mrs. George Petit (Social Life Committee) wondered
if the Msgr. had reached any decision regarding the
PTA's request that a sheltered bicycle rack be attached
to the back wall of the rectory garage to keep the ice
and snow off the children's bikes. Her own daughter,
she said, had actually frozen to her bike seat just last
week and had to be taken inside the house, bike and all,
to thaw loose.

Msgr. said yes, he had reached a decision, and it was no.
First of all, he said, the rectory garage was heated and
this required a special kind of insulated siding which
was easily cracked and the kids would undoubtedly ram
their bikes into it. Secondly, he was not about to provide
a convenient and hidden place right on the playground

where the boys could smoke and commit other immoral acts; and thirdly, if Mrs. Petit would see to it that her daughter was modestly dressed it wouldn't be possible for her to freeze to her bike seat.

Mrs. Petit left the meeting.

Mr. Porash again said something which the secretary missed.

Dr. Barnes then thanked the Msgr. for sparing the Council so much of his time as we all understood that he was a very busy man. The Msgr. said it was his pleasure entirely and that any member of the Council should feel free to approach him at any time between meetings except on Wednesday which was his day off.

Dr. Barnes then asked for a motion to adjourn. Msgr. seconded.

Galileo Re-Tried

PADUA, AUGUST 1—In one of the most closely watched trials of the past week, Italian scientist Galileo Galilei today rejected the Catholic Church's attempt to reinstate in its good graces his theory (now widely held by Protestants and Jews) that the earth revolves around the sun.

"If the Church said I was wrong, then I was wrong," said the four-hundred-four-year-old mathematician (who is credited with formulating the laws of the pendulum, the free fall of objects and the flight of projectiles). "I abjured and recanted the theory of the earth's motion in 1633 and I see no reason to change my stand now," he said at a press conference following today's trial by a special blue ribbon panel of inquisitors which met in closed session here in the private chambers of the Grand Inquisitor.

"That theory was thought up by Copernicus in the first place," the gray-bearded thinker said, "and for a while I thought he was on the right track. Where I went wrong was in teaching it as an established fact when I never had any mathematical proof. And I did so in the face of scripture, tradition and against the Holy Father's express wish that I cease and desist. I don't see what all the fuss is about. People still think of sunrise and sunset—what's the difference which motion causes it."

Said a spokesman for the inquisition: "We are most

distressed by Dr. Galileo's stand. It is seldom that the Church gives a man a second chance. We thought he would be delighted at this opportunity to undo the harm he did so wrongfully teaching the truth before the Church had a chance to discover it for itself. But Dr. Galileo has proved to be a most obdurate son of the Church. It's a shame. In the old days we would have had no difficulty making him see things our way."

Xavier Rynne, a correspondent for the *New Yorker* magazine, who claims to have gained access to today's hearing, reports that Galileo denounced the members of the court as "turncoats and underminers of the faith." "He gave them holy hell," said Rynne, who is widely known for his colorful reporting of the Second Vatican Council. "He told them that they were the ones who should be brought to trial for questioning a decision of the Church at a time when papal authority and the Magisterium were already under attack by 'pinkos, free-thinkers, theological perverts and the minions of scientific materialism.' "

According to Rynne, Galileo refused to hear a special plea from Cardinal Koenig or to meet with a delegation of Catholic Nobel Prize-winners who had flown here secretly to honor the scientist at a banquet following the trial.

In Uppsala, news of the trial was received with mixed emotions. Cries of "Three cheers for Galileo!" and "revisionist dog!" swept back and forth across the floor of the assembly and several fist fights were reported. A highly placed spokesman for the World Council of Churches, who requested that he not be identified, said,

"I could have told them not to bother—once a Catholic, always a Catholic. If anyone still thinks that ecumenism is more than a paper tiger, this should convince him."

In Rome, observers close to the Vatican told of a brief flurry of unusual activity around the papal chambers and noted that all papal audiences had been cancelled for the balance of the week. An editor of *L'Osservatore Romano*, official organ of the Vatican, declined to comment pending knowledge of what his opinion was going to be.

Meanwhile from Paris, word came that General de Gaulle, who had been following reports of the trial by transistor radio from atop the Sorbonne, had commented: "The truth has been served; the sun, as always, continues to revolve about me."

I Remember Papa

TWO days in bed with a sneaky virus and a copy of the Hemingway novel *Islands in the Stream* and I began to think the thermometer was a fishing rod. There were times when I must have been delirious because one stretch of eighteen pages seemed to have the hero, an internationally famous painter named Thomas Hudson, talking to and about his pet cats. Fish, cats, lots of drinks, a goldhearted prostitute, bars, boats, fights and a rousing but fatal chase after the crew of a sunken U-boat all mixed up with those tiny timepills exploding in my stomach. I didn't catch a thing trolling off the end of the bed.

No doubt the critics will be after this one like sharks. It goes to 466 pages and can't fight back—posthumous Papa resurrected by Miss Mary and Charles Scribner, Jr., for $10 and the Book-of-the-Month-Club. I can't help it. I liked it. It killed the virus.

In *Notes from a Sea Diary*, a book designed to scuttle all the land-bound critics who helped drive Hemingway to bay in front of his own shotgun, Nelson Algren says that he met Ernest only once, and briefly. But he remembers distinctly that Hemingway gave him a portentous message: "It is now 2030 hours." Algren got that during a Christmas visit at the *finca* outside Havana and still liked Hemingway. But hell, I knew Hemingway a lot less well than that and I liked him too.

✿   ✿   ✿

"There lies Heeemingway boat," the Havana cop with a submachine gun on his lap told me as we were going sixty along the waterfront.

"The Pilar?" I responded knowledgeably, opening my eyes in a brave but tardy effort to identify the spot. I told myself that I'd come back and hang around in the hope that Hemingway would arrive with Ava Gardner and Ingrid Bergman and offer to take me fishing with him. He was supposed to have a soft spot for servicemen. There was always the chance. But what if he took me and I didn't fish bravely and well and truly disgraced myself? At the moment it was enough to have ridden by the Pilar in a police car, scattering pedestrians like mullet in our wake. It turned out to be a very Hemingway sort of day for me. If I'd had his complete works in compact form I would have eaten them for courage. Batista's Havana in 1954 was a good place to separate editors and critics from real writers.

Shore Patrol Officer for twenty-four hours in one of the off-limits precincts around Las Animas Hospital—a token gesture, an Ensign and Chief Petty Officer to count the bodies and save the embassy a sticky phone call at 3 A.M. Some enterprising researcher in the ship's office made the discovery that I'd had two years of college Spanish and would be just the man to unsnarl the legal difficulties resulting from locking up half the sailors from three visiting American ships. Had they bothered to consult me they would have learned that my two-years of Spanish wasn't good enough to obtain basic necessities, much less preserve international relations. Working up a bad tourist blister the day before, I had tried to purchase a band-aid from two shops and a corner stall. In each instance I had dramatically pointed to my foot and asked for "un bandito." What I got were two contraceptives and a bag of potato chips. I tried to explain that being Catholic I couldn't use the rubber goods and that the chips were too salty, but the proprietors only shrugged and walked away.

The cops ran us around the district by way of reconnaissance for the evening patrol. Thirty-seven bars and fourteen houses but everything, at this afternoon hour, calm and peaceful—not an American sailor in sight. I cheered up. Off limits must mean off limits. But the Chief Petty Officer, a hardbitten man, kept right on making notes of the addresses of all the houses.

We arrived at precinct headquarters about five. It was a marvellous building in pink marble, just a shade less grand than the Taj Mahal. They showed me to an empty desk. I put my whistle and clipboard on it and sat down. Law and order was going to be a snap. The Chief disappeared.

I watched the night shift come in. Playful fellows, one and all, they horsed around with loaded Thompsons. A little muzzle-feint here, a little barrel-jab there. Then they stood the guns up in a row against the marble wall about thirty feet from me. (It was o.k., though, because the butts rested on the equally slick marble floor.) I looked for things under my desk. That was the first of many mistakes I would make. There was a none-too-ancient human skull down there with a big hole in it where none should have been; a sandwich wrapped in brown paper was stuck between the jaws. I was glad I didn't find a whistle around its no-neck but decided I'd forego the sandwich.

Everybody stopped horsing around when the Commandante, a truly elegant man in a uniform that would make Nixon drool, came out to look over the shift. It was Friday night and he was clearly on his way back to the fort but, spotting me behind my desk (no mean trick in itself), he graciously invited me into his office. Nixon would have coveted that, too. It was so big it had an horizon. Over the fire place was an oil of Batista wearing a uniform only slightly grander than the Commandante's. The one stripe on my rumpled coat shriveled up and died.

El Cid offered me a cigar which I took, but no brandy from the cutglass decanter on his desk, which I would have taken too. Basil Rathbone couldn't have come across the language barrier better. "An unpleasant duty, but a necessary one that we both perform," he told me. He made it crystal clear that the part of Havana I would be scanning was not his neighborhood. He had a boy in a Catholic military school in Georgia, a sailing yacht and a hacienda in the suburbs. He concluded by indicating, with great tact, that the best thing I could do would be not to interfere, leave everything to his men and simply stay out of the way. It sounded like great advice so I thanked him and went out to look for the Chief.

It took me three hours to find him. He was having a beer in the parlor of the busiest house in the district. I found it by following the steady stream of sailors moving in and out the door. These rascals were all out of bounds but didn't seem a bit disturbed by the big SP armband I was wearing. But who would catch the end of the stick when the word got back to headquarters? Me, that was who.

I got in line and worked my way upstairs where I discovered the Chief. He'd made a lot of friends in a short time it seemed, and he assured them that I was not the sort to make trouble. The madame smiled at me and with a sweep of her bangled arm indicated that I should take my pick of the girls in the room, "on the house"— an etymological irony which escaped me at the moment. I yelled at the Chief to get the hell back to the station and fled into the night.

Back at my desk I called Shore Patrol Headquarters and told them that the whole fleet was out of bounds to the man. How many of them should I arrest? Could I please have some help, as the Chief wasn't working out too well? The man on the other end of the line yawned and asked if there was a brawl in any of the houses? Was there riot and bloodshed on the streets? Was anybody complaining about being overcharged? Hadn't they offered me freebies? No? Then what the hell was I bothering headquarters about? He hung up.

I still had visions of a court martial with me as the star. Finally, I remembered what the Commandante had told me about leaving everything to his men. A word to the duty officer and all would be well. But the Commandante's men were all occupied back in the cell-block. They had "arrested" a half-dozen prostitutes, put them into individual cells, and were collecting money from a line of male "visitors" queued up outside the back door. No wonder the Commandante could afford the tuition at a Catholic school.

I went back to my desk and sat down. What would Hemingway do in such a situation, I asked myself. I got no answer so I decided to consult with my friend underneath the desk. The sandwich was gone from his mouth, but he still wasn't talking. It was way past 2030 hours so I decided to join him and went to sleep with my whistle and clipboard close at hand, ready for instant action against the forces of corruption everywhere.

✷   ✷   ✷

I never did go back and stand waiting by the Pilar. Somebody told me later that Hemingway was out of the country then, anyway. I did take one of the ship's boats to troll for marlin in the Gulf Stream out beyond the Morro. They were there in abundance, great curved fins darting on all sides of us. And sure enough, I missed them all, bravely and truly and well.

Six Versions of a Prayer You've Heard Somewhere

HIPPIE
OR MALCOLM BOYD VERSION

Hey Dad!
You're really out there,
Your name's a blast.
Make our scene as cool as yours.
Spread
A little bread around our pads,
But don't zap us, like,
We don't burn straights when they bug us.
From work in all its forms,
Please steer us clear.
And keep Ronald Reagan off our backs.
How 'bout it, man?

TRADITIONALIST VERSION

Right Reverend God,
Who resides in that big chancery in the sky,
Live up to your Old Testament reputation
And get things back in order here below.
Give baptized, practicing Catholics
Their rights and privileges,
And forive us for Vatican II,
Just as we will try to forgive
Those sneaky Jews.
Lead us not into experimental liturgies
But deliver us from the Dutch Catechism.
Amen.

EMERGED LAYMAN'S VERSION

Dear Chairman of the People of:
May your name head all petitions,
Your discussion club thrive,
Your pastor admit,
He's out of it.
Give us equal voice to say
Who shall come and who will stay,
As that triumphant bishop whom
We can forget but not forgive
For leading us into building drives.
But deliver us from lay teachers.
Bye.
(*Enclosed find 6 tickets for the CFM Dance*).

NEW BREED PRIEST'S VERSION

Celibate Father, here's your chance
To join our union here below
And show
The Ordinary how you bleed
For our *so* pressing need.
Give us salaries, cars and things,
But no rigid laws or structures,
Please nota.
Yet keep us fairly close to mom,
And spare us from the mission quota.
O.K.?

ADMINISTRATIVE
OR L. B. J. VERSION

My fellow American
In Neutral Outer Space,
May you get a better press than me.
Your Great Society spend and spend,
Your term in office never end.
Balance our budget if you can,
And forgive us our cookouts
As we forgive Bobby Baker.
Thanks for leading
Linda Bird past George Hamilton
And deliver us from the Kennedys.
Amen, you all.
(P.S. Can't you do something about Sam Houston?)

ALL PURPOSE LIBERAL OR
NATIONAL CATHOLIC REPORTER VERSION

You, who until Leslie Dewart can come up
With something better, we'll call God,
About this oversimplified concept of heaven.
Give up your ancient authoritarianism
And try to be more open, like us.
Bread alone is not enough to cope
With all the varieties of our unrest,
Especially under one species.
We'll try our patient utmost to remain
Within the historical outpost of your domain
(But you might think about meeting us
     halfway).
May all old pastors die off sickly,
and collegiality come most quickly.
End.

Life with Father

Dear Ann Blanders:

Recently I left the Roman Catholic priesthood to marry a widow with five children. A number of my former colleagues joined the bishop in warning me that I was making a stupid mistake and that any forty-six-year-old bachelor, let alone one who had been a priest and pastor, would have enormous difficulties adjusting to family life. Well, they were wrong, and I hope you'll publish this letter for the benefit of all those disenchanted priests who've let the kill-joy prophets of doom talk them out of marrying.

In the beginning, I'll admit, it was a trifle difficult. Women, as you know, are curious, prideful creatures not much good at reasoning things through or tackling problems in a practical, business-like way. My wife, for instance, had no money sense at all. She took it for granted that she would have ready access to my income through a joint checking account, charge cards and a non-accountable petty-cash fund. She even demanded to know how much I made in my new job as manager of the large construction firm which hired me as soon as I let my availability be known. (That's another song-and-dance my former priest friends gave me—that a pastor isn't qualified for a comparable job in the secular world.) It didn't take me long to explain the voucher and centralized purchasing system I've used with such

singular success over the years. A bill without a purchase order approved by me means a trip back to the
store, I can tell you that!

And the poor dear had some notion that we'd be taking
vacations together, as a family! The places in Florida
where I stay won't even take curates, let alone children
and dogs. I had to explain that there simply wouldn't be
any point in taking a vacation *with* your family. The
whole point is to get away from day-to-day problems.
Why, I'd just as soon take along a bishop! She took this
badly for a while, I must say, but felt considerably better when I gave her Wednesday afternoons off with the
use of the car until five-thirty.

She also failed to understand why my mother and my
former housekeeper had to move in with us after the
honeymoon. A man's relationship with his mother is
sacred, of course, and now that I don't have to live apart
from her anymore I was simply fulfilling the natural law
by keeping her close to me where she belongs. The
housekeeper knows how I like my food prepared and
my pajamas ironed. I wouldn't dream of throwing my
always delicate digestion open to the ravages of the
wanton succession of hot dogs and hamburgers which
my wife prepares for the children.

We have separate rooms, of course. Sex is all well and
good and I enjoy it as much as the next man. But after
a simple time and motion study it was obvious that it
occupies a tiny fraction of a married couple's time.
Meanwhile, there's no reason to spoil a restful night's

sleep. It's really not terribly healthy to pass a complete night in close proximity to another human being. Still, spontaneity in these matters is terribly important—one can't simply set a schedule and follow if inflexibly. I solved the problem quite neatly, I think, by installing some leftover confessional lights outside our respective bedroom doors. One light on is a question; two lights on, consensus.

The much-dreaded chaos of life with five children was quite easily managed. My regular bulletin is issued every Sunday morning (*The Family Chimes*, I call it) and lists everything from meals to bath times. The children submit their scheduled activities as well as special requests for parties, dates, transportation, etc., to me by Wednesday evening. All approved events are then scheduled chronologically and published. If it's not published they can assume that permission has been withheld. No exceptions are ever made, of course. *The Chimes* also lists the hours for the regularly weekly conference I grant to each child. It has solved all our problems quite handily. My only concern at the moment is with selling advertising spots on the back cover to local merchants. They'll come around in time.

There's a great deal more I could tell you, but by now the point should be obvious: marriage and family life present no problems to the former priest that can't be solved by reason, sound management and a firm pastoral hand. The best endorsement of my methods I can offer comes from my wife who is understandably happy with the way things have worked out. If she's told me once, she's told me a thousand times: "You're just too much, you know that don't you!"

A Satisfied Former Celibate

Issues That
Divide the Panel

Dramatis Personae:

ROBERT ADROIT—Editor of *The National Catholic Revealer*, convener and moderator of the Panel.

REV. ANDREW M. SURVEY—Author, columnist and sociologist, Father Survey has many strings for his bow, or many bows for his string, depending on how you see it.

MISS JACQUELINE OVERWALL—Educator, soul-searcher, innovator and scene-stealer, Miss Overwall is so much in the news these days that people sometimes have difficulty knowing where else she is.

ARCHBISHOP DIRE—In the face of compelling pressures toward change, the affable and knowledgeable Archbishop has refused to settle for anything less than being a member of the hierarchy.

BRENT BOMBSHELL—The articulate editor of the recently founded magazine *Atrophy*, Mr. Bombshell is perhaps best known for his scheme to force time to run backwards or, failing that, at least to stand still.

DANIEL LIBERALHAND—Dynamic young scholar, journalist and author of a number of widely discussed books including the controversial *Dishonesty in the Diaspora*.

DR. GEORGE SCHOLASTIC—Years of experience in education, balanced wisdom, a reputation for coming through sticky situations without any gum on his soles—these are the qualities which Dr. Scholastic brings to the Panel.

Transcription:

MR. ADROIT: On the one hand, as you all know, or on the other hand, as you may not know, we're gathered here to discuss the most burning issues of the day . . .

FATHER SURVEY: Day? What Day? Let's be specific. If we're going to begin with a lot of vague generalities, I'm going to take my statistics and go home.

MR. ADROIT: Well, then, this day—today . . .

ARCHBISHOP DIRE: I can't say that I care much for your use of that word "burning." It smacks of alarmism and sensationalism. Why disturb people unnecessarily?

MR. LIBERALHAND: Does the Archbishop mean to imply that people aren't already badly disturbed?

MISS OVERWALL: I sense a certain tension here—my feminine intuition tells me that this is not the way we should begin. Let's all think positively. Aside from Mr. Bombshell who is hopelessly out of it—though I don't for a moment deny his sincerity—I suspect that we could all find . . .

MR. BOMBSHELL: Well if you're in it, I'm just as glad to be out. But I think you've got it just backwards. At least I didn't run out on . . .

MR. ADROIT: Hold on! Let's not get personal. We're here to talk about issues and we'd better get on with it. I've drawn up a list of seven . . .

DR. SCHOLASTIC: I wonder if "issues" is precisely the term we should be using. I think in the public mind it's too much identified with politics. A more useful term might be realized if we examined the etymology of . . .

FATHER SURVEY: And how, pray tell, did you arrive at the number seven? What makes you think there aren't five, or fifty? I'd like to see your data.

MR. LIBERALHAND: And I resent your arbitrary decision against personalism. What is the people of God if it isn't an open personal interchange? I thought this sort of sterile angelism was buried with Pius IX.

MR. BOMBSHELL: I take it, then, that Mr. Liberalhand doesn't believe in angels? I suppose Michael, Gabriel and Raphael were really just ordinary people of God who managed to grow wings. And while you're correcting the magisterium would you mind explaining how you manage to bury a pure spirit in the first place?

MISS OVERWALL: Really, Mr. Bombshell, you have a streak of literalism in you a yard wide. Where's your flexibility, your feel for analogy? I really think you ought to move out of your defensive crouch and let the free interplay of ideas sweep over you. Why even the Archbishop knows that what Mr. Liberalhand meant was . . .

ARCHBISHOP DIRE: Please don't feel constrained to patronize me, Miss Overwall. I may not be blessed with your feminine instincts but I can take care of myself. I assure you. Now, if you'll all simply submit your questions in writing . . .

MR. ADROIT: No, no, no! This is all being recorded for transcription.

FATHER SURVEY: You weren't actually dreaming of publishing this verbal Dunkirk?

DR. SCHOLASTIC: I'd be remiss if I didn't say that I think the whole concept might profit from a careful re-thinking.

MR. LIBERALHAND: I won't submit a thing in writing; it's an outdated medium of communication.

MISS OVERWALL: I intuit an impasse. If you'll excuse me, I've got to get my hair arranged for a network television appearance. But I want you to know how terribly open I feel toward you all.

MR. BOMBSHELL: I've got to see a man about a heresy.

MR. ADROIT: Oh well, I can probably get an editorial out of it, anyway.

FATHER SURVEY: I've got no objection to opinion as long as it's clearly labeled.

ARCHBISHOP DIRE: *Ite Panel Est!*

PEOPLE OF GOD: *Deo Gratias!*

How Green
Was My Fairway

(The Real Father Urban Stands Up)

Rev. John Kelleher
Clementine Fathers
St. Clement's Hill
Deusterhaus, Minnesota

Dear Jack,

This is a letter I was hoping I wouldn't have to write. Not that I wasn't going to drop you a line in a few days, anyway, but I didn't want it to be like this, under duress. I won't try to kid you, I've known I'd have some explaining to do ever since September when I ran across an ad announcing publication of a novel called—Hang on to your nine-iron!—*Morte D'Urban* by an author named J. F. Powers. In spite of the title I wouldn't have given it a second thought if it hadn't been for the author's name. Remember how you told me you felt when you first heard about Pearl Harbor—a combination of blind rage and nausea. Well that's how I felt when I read that ad, only more so, since I didn't know how bad the damage was going to be.

All I knew was that I had spent an evening a couple of years back with a character named Jim Powers (I still haven't found out what the "F" stands for; probably

Freemason) and that now here was a novel "about a priest who tried to beat the world at its own game," which had my name mixed up in the title. Right then, as I told the Provincial (I put off telling him as long as I could in the hope that the book would drop out of sight before he got wind of it—it's a first novel—but *Time* had to review it and, as we all know from reading his column in *The Clementine*, the Provincial definitely reads *Time*: "Too little and too lightly regarded by most Catholics, the Holy Season of Advent next week will begin without most of them even being aware of the fact."), I knew I had been sold down the river by one of the smoothest con-men to don the habit since Richelieu. Obviously, I don't mean Powers; you don't blame the bullet for the hole in your back. I don't like to tie name tags to my black tales, but since you and Wilf and almost everybody else in the Order are involved (you're one of the main characters, by the way) you've got a right to know who fingered you. None other than that most frequent user of the Hill's fairways, our mutual friend, Father Feld.

Ever since the weekend I took him for three straight rounds (his putting was off, he said, because he'd burned his right palm filling a red hot censer at Forty Hours Devotion earlier in the week) I knew I wasn't heading up his list of favorite people. But I guess I really poured salt on a boil when I kidded him about the Christian Family Movement one day during the time I was pinch-hitting at St. Monica's. A lot of the bigger bucks in the diocese had come around to say goodbye to Phil (the Pastor) and Monsignor Renton before they left on vacation, Feld among them. We were all sitting around sampling some of the liquid assets one of the more thoughtful parishioners had sent over in a plain brown wicker hamper ("Bon Voyage to a real swell Pastor"), talking a little shop. Feld's palm must still have been bothering him a lot, because he kept it wrapped around a cold glass practically continuously. It wasn't long before he got expansive and told how he was the one who had really gotten CFM off the ground in the Diocese, more or less over the Bishop's dead body.

I would have let it go, but somebody who should have known better had dragged along a matched pair of first assignment curates, still pale and liberal from the seminary, and they sat there listening to Feld as if he had been dictating *Rerum Novarum* on the spot, so I had to throw a harpoon. It had been a long hard week taking over the keys to Phil's kingdom, and I had shaken hands with Johnny Walker a few times myself, so it was a pretty blunt instrument I used; something about the Bishop's having told me that the only way he could ever manage to get anything new started in the Diocese was to act like he was dead set against it.

If looks could keep you in Purgatory, the one Feld gave me would have paid my dues for a century or two, and seeing that I'd gotten onto his green, I used my best pulpit voice to ask Monsignor Renton if he'd heard how the little boy in religion class had defined CFM. (You've heard that one: "Can't Find Mamma—she's gone to a meeting.") Feld was still too conscious of his new-found disciples to blow up. He gave me a tight little smile, the kind missionaries say you can see on the face of a cobra just before it strikes, and left.

Well, aside from giving myself a few penalty strokes for lack of charity, I didn't give the matter another thought. I should have, especially when Feld called up about two weeks later with his mouth full of honey and told me that he thought he was on to something really big in the way of a publicity break for the Order. He had run into an old college friend of his, a free-lance writer who regularly had his stuff published in the big magazines. He said they'd gotten to talking about new developments in the Diocese and that he had told his friend all about the Clementines coming in and starting a retreat house and what a wonderful thing the Hill could develop into, *and* that his friend had immediately wondered if there might not be a good story in it.

That hooked me, of course, since Feld knew that right then I would have stood on my head for even a paragraph in the Deusterhaus *Daily Dairyman* and he was larding every sentence with names like *Post, Life* and *Look*. He got to toying with me at the end, wondering if, just as a personal favor to him, I could spare a few hours to talk to his friend that evening? You've got to be really sure of yourself to lay on the expensive spread like that. He knew I'd have made time for his friend during my own mother's canonization, if need be. Even then he couldn't stop, but fell all over himself thanking me, and all the while I kept right on swimming for the deep water, not even feeling the plug in my mouth.

"Friend," of course, turned out to be good old Jim Powers and I still can't do more than regret that there are men in the world who have to make their living the way he does. I understand he has a big family and I guess it's less risky than blackmail and cleaner than digging up cadavers. I won't bore you with the details of how I played into his hands that night; suffice it to say that given Powers' peculiar talents ("We've got to get behind the scenes, Father"), I couldn't have done more for his novel if I had handed it to him, page at a time, typed double-space and all ready to go.

Feld came by to collect him a little after midnight, looking as pleased with himself as if he'd just converted Russia single-handedly. We all had a night-cap with both of them having an increasingly hard time keeping their faces straight (I thought they were just happy about a job well done; which, of course, they were). Really, looking back at the whole thing, I think the hardest thing to swallow (the book itself still doesn't seem real to me) is the memory of that farewell scene on the front porch of St. Monica's Rectory. I clasped Powers' hand in both of mine and told him that St. Clement was probably even then polishing up a crown for him; Feld, I actually embraced, and asked what I had ever done to deserve such a kindness. It was stickier than the ending of *Goodbye, Mr. Chips!* I don't know how they did it, but they both managed to make it off the porch and into Feld's car without breaking up.

That's all I heard about it (thank God, I was at least able to restrain myself from asking Feld if he'd heard which magazine would be carrying the article) until I saw that ad in September. Two days later I got a copy of the book in the mail with a little inscription scrawled on the flyleaf:

> Abou Ben Urban,
> May his drive decrease,
> Awoke one day
> From a deep dream . . .
> —from all the gang at CFM
>   (Cry For Mercy)

For a few days after he read the book, the Provincial didn't say anything; in fact, he hardly moved. Then he called me in and asked if I thought, (1) Was there any chance at all of getting the thing put on the Index, fast? and (2) Did Canon Law permit a religious order to sue for libel? I told him "No" on both counts and that there was nothing we could do but grin and bear it in the true spirit of Christian humility.

I sincerely hope that you and Wilf will be able to look at it the same way, though I don't think it would hurt to go down to the locker room ("We don't need locks here at St. Clement's Hill, men") and take Father Feld's new set of Arnold Palmer woods out to the lake and see if they will float. It seems the very least we could do, considering that we've already been hit on both cheeks.

> As ever,
> (Rev.) Urban Roche

Juventutem Meam

THE thing is, of course, that Catholic kids today have got it hopelessly soft. To begin with, they don't have to go to Mass every day like we did—eight years at eight o'clock, girls in front, boys in back where Sister could keep an eye on them. Somewhere along about the sixth grade, the grip of the Depression relented and we got padded kneelers and I'm here to tell you that I haven't gloried in any physical sensation, including sex, half as much as the first time I settled my ravaged knees into that plastic-covered rubber. Before that you just hung in there, shifting knees and pulling up until your knuckles turned white. I wasn't heavy enough (in those days) to be much good at the sport of elbow-tension, which was how we killed the longest stretch of kneeling time between the Sanctus and the Agnus Dei. What you did was to get the boy at each end of the pew to lock his hands and brace one elbow against the corner post. Then the next guy in locked his hands and braced his elbows against those of the guys on each side of him so that you got this terrific pressure building up without it looking like anything was going on. Then, if you did it right, the weakest link in the chain would shoot straight up in the air about two feet. It was generally me and it was generally right before the elevation. ("Bless me Father, I committed adultery with others, of the same sex, in Church, during Mass.")

If you went to communion you got to eat breakfast

in the classroom while the non-receivers (generally the fruit of mixed marriages) had to start working a bunch of arithmetic problems. Also, you got a gold star on your chart, too, but that was nothing compared to eating a chocolate covered donut while others looked for impossible common denominators. We had a very pious class.

Certain guys who, in later life, turn out to be very successful corporation executives are born to be Traffic Guards. They are let out of class early to assume their posts and get to wear white chest straps and silver badges and are generally pukes. Others, like me, are made into Mass servers, and are usually nice guys who don't ever amount to much. They turned you into servers early in those days on the theory that younger boys were purer. By the time you hit puberty you were washed up and burnt out. So, before I learned the multiplication tables I was taught to rattle off the Latin responses to the Mass, which, like riding a bike, you never forget, no matter how hard you try. My wife tells me I still mumble Latin in my sleep occasionally, when I'm exhausted or have been particularly nasty to the kids.

In addition to the parish church, our school supplied servers for the Little Sisters of the Poor Home for the Aged and to the Poor Clare Cloistered Convent. We worked on three-week shifts, rotating through the three places with a week off between shifts. I've married and buried the population equivalent of a good sized town and lit enough candles to make Father Keller and his Christophers cry quits. The softest touch was the parish church, because it was reasonably warm in the winter and the earliest Mass was at 6:30. The Little Sisters of the Poor, on the other hand, were just that, and they kept their old people healthy by sparing them the dehydrating effects of central heating. Everything was scrubbed to the nub but everything nonetheless smelled very badly. You had to change from your street shoes to sneakers so you wouldn't scratch the sanctuary floor. And the old folks inevitably found your shoes and removed the laces, no matter where you hid them or how hard you knotted them together.

But the real adventure was the Poor Clare Convent. Their Mass was at six which meant a five o'clock reveille and a long bike-ride across half the town. The convent, or monastery as it was called, occupied a good part of a city block and was completely enclosed by a ten-foot brick wall. When the Ku Klux Klan made its latter-day revival in the Midwest there had been some nastiness aimed at the Poor Clares for being strange, secretive and Catholic. After a cross was burned in front of the convent gate, the Knights of Columbus turned out the next day and topped off the wall with jagged pieces of beer bottles (which the Knights somehow know where to find) set in mortar. That had been twenty-five years earlier but the wall and the broken glass still stood as a reminder that ecumenism had still to overcome.

To wheel up on a pitch-black winter morning, open the iron gates and commit yourself to the inner fastness was roughly equivalent to solo trick-or-treating at Dracula's castle. Inside a little arched doorway was a small room where your cassock and surplice had been laid out by invisible hands. The little room opened into the sanctuary which was itself nothing but a larger room with no church in the front of it. Instead there were two massive grilles covered by long velvet drapes. The Poor Clares were back there chanting away in what must have been beautiful form, but which scared what little hell there was left out of me.

After I suited up I went out and rang a brass bell and lit the candles. Then old Father Louis, who always appeared from his own little room on the other side of the sanctuary, would come out and say Mass. The curtains never opened but I was conscious of ranked tiers of Sisters with their eyes peeled for the least fidget or twitch. Father Louis had come from the Old Country a long time ago but English was always going to sit uncomfortably on his German tongue. His big and enduring concern was the Marxist conspiracy. He preached on this to the cloistered nuns, warning them over and over against the dangers of becoming infected by atheistic Communism. Communists were everywhere at work undermining the bulwark of Mother Church. Eternal vigilance was the only cure. I got so I saw Communists behind every telephone pole and mailbox. The place was crawling with them, all trying to get at the sisters.

I worried about them but I wasn't above trying to sneak glimpses of their faces when they received communion through a little gold door in the wall. Father Louis generally blocked my view, but I saw a nose once or twice, and part of a mouth. ("Bless me Father, I looked at consecrated virgins.") There was a kindly extern Sister but she obviously wasn't happy about being out front and materialized only infrequently. At Christmas and Easter a handsome basket of candy was set out by my cassock.

Then one night my mother got a call. One of the Poor Clare's had died and I had been selected to assist at the funeral, along with two other long-time servers. We convened next morning and, after the Funeral Mass, Sister Extern handed me the processional cross. But where would we process to? Only then it dawned on me that we were going to be admitted to the inner sanctum.

In the sanctuary the drapes were suddenly pulled apart and the great grille swung open. Like a missionary Alice going through the glass I held the six-foot cross in front of me and stepped into the unknown. There were nuns, fewer than I'd imagined, but lined up in rows with partial black veils covering pale faces. The first huge and almost empty room opened into a long corridor which we traversed Indian-file behind a guiding Sister who never recognized our presence by so much as a nod. Right angle down another corridor, up some steps and down more until I was hopelessly turned around. Finally we went through a narrow archway and down stone steps that wound around and around. They ended in a large crypt. At the far end the dead nun was laid out flat on the floor resting on a large board. A plain wooden coffin sat against the wall directly under the deep hole which had been opened to receive it. A large bucket of steaming wet mortar with a trowel stuck in it rounded out the gala setting.

The dead nun had no veil on, and there was just enough space between her head and the end of the room for me to plant myself and the cross. Father Louis and my colleagues took up their stand at her feet. Father Louis began his prayers, punctuating them with with heavy splats of holy water which criss-crossed the dead nun's habit like machinegun bullets. I had never seen a dead person at such close quarters, and the finality of "deadness" came home to me emphatically as I watched the holy water roll down that stony forehead and into the corner of an unblinking eye.

There was not a tear to be seen in any other eye, however, nor any sobs to be heard. The only sound was Father Louis droning on and on in his guttural Latin. When he was done, two elderly caretakers shuffled in, picked up the board, nun and all, put it into the coffin, nailed the lid shut, slid it into the wall and, while we trooped back up the winding steps, began to splash on the mortar. Nobody could accuse those nuns of getting sentimental about death—I'd seen puppies buried with more loving care. I didn't understand, of course, but it remains one of the most cold-blooded sights I've ever witnessed.

It wasn't long afterwards that puberty began to manifest its awful effects upon my voice and thus revealed to be on the verge of concupiscence, I was cashiered from the ranks of servers forever.

And not a day too soon.

Our Parish Council Meets Sex Education or *I Was Furious (Purple)*

Minutes of an extraordinary meeting of the St. Prometheus Parish Council convened at the special request of the Right Reverend George McMann, pastor and honorary chairman of the Council. All members of the board were present, plus a non-voting attendance of interested parties numbering approximately 680 (janitor's estimate) or virtually the entire registered adult population of the parish. The meeting was called to order at 8:30 p.m. in the school gym-cafeteria complex by Dr. Clive Barnes, D.D.S., council president, who introduced Monsignor McMann as the first, and as it happened, only speaker of the evening.

MSGR. McMANN: Well, we all turned out for this one, didn't we? You don't have to be Hans Kung or Karl Rahner to figure out that this isn't Forty Hours Devotion. I haven't seen so many of you in one spot at one time since we played ten-dollar-a-card bingo for that yellow Caddy back in '57. In my seminary days old Father Burke, God rest his tough old soul, used to tell us:

"There's nothing like sex or money to bring'em up out of the woodwork." And I was still so wet behind the ears that I didn't know what he meant.

But I didn't come all the way back from Arizona to joke. Any time I interrupt my winter vacation you can bet it's no laughing matter. Next to atheistic Communism, sex is the most disgusting, insidious force at work in the world today. Now I know that a lot of you out there don't take sin very seriously anymore. I know that there are women in this parish who swallow contraceptive pills and then parade up to Communion on Sunday morning like so many lilies of the valley. They've got a million cute little excuses for the confessional—when they bother to confess it at all. The pill regulates this and stabilizes that, and doctor so-and-so says they simply couldn't live without it. But they know and I know that they're taking them because they want to have their cake and eat it too. Disgusting pandering to animal appetites—that's all it is!

No, I can't expect people who laugh and sneer at the teaching of our infallible Holy Father to worry about sex, or Communism, for that matter. And the two are more closely linked than some of you wise-guy liberals out there realize. It wasn't the John Birch Society that introduced sex education for innocent little grade school children, I can tell you that. The fact that the Commies have worked their will on the public school system doesn't surprise me in the least. I'm not surprised, either, that now they're trying to infect the last bastion of decency left in this country—our good white

Catholic schools. What does surprise and shock me is to see some of our very own sisters and one of my own assistants not only taken in by the plot but working actively to foment it. How far they're actually involved in this I haven't been able to determine but if I were them I wouldn't be ordering any return address labels for next year.

I want to stop right here and now and thank Doctor Barnes not just for calling this special meeting tonight but for phoning me long distance to let me know what was going on back here. It's getting so a person can't get away for a few weeks without things going to hell on wheels. As I understand it, all the children in the sixth, seventh and eighth grades were to be exposed to a series of films called "The Great Adventure," which is the fancy name some pervert thought up to camouflage some of the filthiest sex movies you can imagine. Some people actually wanted to screen those films here tonight "so the parents can decide for themselves," but I can assure you that I'm not going to have that on my conscience or put a lot of innocent people in the direct occasion of serious mortal sin.

You'll just have to take the word of an old and experienced confessor that these films—and there are so-called "correlated reading materials" as well, just as filthy—that this stuff is not kidding around about birds, bees, flowers and storks. No sir and no mam! They pull it right straight from the gutter, the real undiluted stuff —male and female private parts in living color; sperm swimming around fertilizing everything in sight; ovaries discharging right before your very eyes; pictures of a baby being born; pictures of nasty little cells in the very act of dividing. That's the sort of stuff they want to project on our classroom walls, right up there under the crucifix, in full view of the statue of Our Blessed Lady conceived without sin!

Now I know that there are many good souls here tonight and I apologize for having to talk of such disgusting things in front of a mixed audience. In the old days a word to the head of the Holy Name Society would have been sufficient. But now we've got collegiality and co-responsibility and it's not always so pleasant, is it? I can see that many of you are genuinely as shocked as I am. If it affects you that way just think what it would do to the tender souls of our little ones.

But there are some here who think I'm old fashioned and authoritarian. One mother even went so far as to tell me that she'd rather have her girl shocked than pregnant. Well, you can ask Dr. Barnes and the members of the Parish Council—most of them—and they'll tell you that I'm as open-minded and progressive as they come. I don't know what-all foolishness I've already gone along with in the past ten years from ripping out our $50,000 Italian marble Communion rail to letting the CCD kids invite Jews and Protestants to the parish teen dance. But I will not, I cannot stand still for this. There will be no "Great Adventure" films shown in our parish school. There will be no sex education courses of any kind in my school—ever—period! You can argue and whine and stamp your liberal-hippie feet until they're sore, but it won't change my mind. There will be no further discussion of the matter and there will be no vote taken here tonight.

Now let's all rise and close the meeting with a prayer to St. Thomas Aquinas who drove the harlot from his room with a burning faggot.

Cardboard Crosier
(by Plimp Georgeton)

WHEN my publisher Arnold Shameless first called to suggest that for my next book I "become" a Catholic bishop, I thought the dear old rascal had finally become dislodged from his tree. By this time I trust it's well-established that I'm no coward, but for a mere layman —not even a Catholic one at that—to undertake to infiltrate the Roman hierarchy was preposterous. I'd need a diocese, a limousine, a chancery office, episcopal ring and a course in fund-raising just for a start. And, without some degree of official cooperation or connivance, it would truly be mission impossible.

I had it in mind to dispose of this wild scheme quickly when I went up to Arnold's office and to offer my own alternative which was to become a Japanese Sumo wrestler. But no sooner than I'd put foot inside the room a voice shouted: "Stop right where you are, Plimp!" I found myself staring into the blinding rays of a spotlight which made it utterly impossible to make out Arnold, or indeed anything else in the office.

"That's him. What do you think?" I heard Arnold say conspiratorily.

A deep, slightly muffled voice replied: "Never do— way too skinny."

Could Arnold have possibly guessed my alternative proposal and rigged this mysterious confrontation to squelch it?

"There must be some *thin* bishops," I heard Arnold say.

"One or two, but they die young—no staying power."

The unknown voice carried a heavy freight of authority. Certainly, here was a man used to having his own way. Could I have under-estimated Arnold's knavery? Had the man actually succeeded in bribing a Catholic bishop into cooperating in this mad plan?

"All right, we'll pad him up a bit then," said Arnold. "Otherwise we'll proceed as agreed?"

"Mmmph!" said the stranger. "It's disgusting what we ex-bishops have to do to survive."

* * *

Three unbelievably arduous weeks later and I was being driven through the streets of Washington, D. C., in a long black Lincoln by a short Irish driver who threaded his way through the morning traffic with appropriate dignity. Dignity appropriate, that is, to the transporting of Bishop Terence O'Laughlin of Metro City, Texas, from his hotel suite to the Quarterly Meeting of the American Bishops. That was the name settled on me by former Bishop X who assured me that things were moving at such a frantic pace that no one would question my appointment and title on the simple grounds that they'd never heard of me or of Metro City, Texas. If questioned, I was to mumble something about a new population cluster around an ultra-secret space complex. My name would be entered illegally on the meeting roster and there would be a name-tag and manila folder just like all the others awaiting me.

My attire had been meticulously tailored and the gold chain which glittered diagonally down over my artificial paunch looked very official. I had learned to smoke thick Havana cigars without choking; I had memorized the names and faces of my fellow bishops, the Apostolic Delegate and a monsignor named George Higgins; I even had a small coat of arms stamped on the inside of my hat and on my attache case—two anchovies rampant on a field of pizza to represent the prime tourist attraction of my titular see of Pepperoni.

The externals were all in order. What worried ex-Bishop X and what we had drilled and practiced into the small hours of the morning were the myriad intangible details which could betray me in a second. Well, we would soon find out how well I'd mastered them. My immediate goal was to gain admittance to the morning's regular closed session—a feat accomplished by no laymen or member of the press in living memory.

The car pulled up under a canopy and I got out. The lobby of the Sheraton was jammed with reporters, priests, a group of nuns carrying signs which read "Sisters for Sex Education," and a dozen or so laymen who had knotted themselves into a group resembling a closed fist and were shouting obscenities at the trail of bishops who were beating their way upstream across the lobby toward the ballroom doors. I assumed a look of sublime indifference which I'd practiced in the mirror and plunged into the maelstrom.

"Good morning, Emmet," I said to the back of the head of a bishop whom I was suddenly thrust against.

I'd had just a glance at his face and was pleased with the resultant instant recognition. He made an effort to identify me but the press was such that he couldn't manage even a glimpse. But the direct familiarity and the carefully honed timbre of my voice were sufficient to convince him that I was indeed a colleague. Bishop X knew his stuff!

"Isn't this disgusting," he threw back at me over his shoulder. "Those nuns should be back in the convent making hosts and I'd turn the fire hoses on that shouting rabble."

He gained another yard with me following his interference closely. (I was desperately afraid my paunch would become detached and move off to the side.) I almost betrayed myself by asking if such chaos prevailed at every meeting but caught myself in time to inquire in a bored tone if he expected anything interesting to come up at the meeting.

"Only the usual bunch of petitions from cry-baby priests," he responded throwing his hip into a waiter carrying a heavy bag. "I did hear that security is tight this morning. Rumor is that some journalist is trying to crash the meeting."

"No!" I gasped, completely reverting to my own voice. Was it all going to be in vain? Had we been betrayed? By whom? Would I be fingered by ex-Bishop X as I approached the credentials table? Another example of the disgusting things "we ex-bishops have to do to survive"? Well, there was no turning back even if I wanted to. We were literally being funneled toward the doors of the ballroom.

Another few feet and I'd be in front of the table. As my line of vision cleared, I noted with horror that it was manned not by the harmless secretary I'd been led to expect, but by three fierce-looking prelates, two of whom I recognized as Cardinals. They were scowling and actually peering suspiciously into the face of each bishop as he freed himself from the mob, picked up his agenda and stepped into the calm of the inner sanctum.

Would they arrest me on the spot? I saw no policeman at hand. Then I remembered tales of the Spanish Inquisition and images of old Plimp being fed to the screw and rack began to surge up. At least Bishop X was nowhere to be seen.

Then Emmet made a final plunge which almost uprooted a potted palm (the Lions could use him at fullback) and broke into the clear. His movement was so sudden that I lost the shelter of his bulk and stood exposed before the table. But just then a man grabbed my arm—a reporter type with a portable tape-recorder in his hand.

"Care to make a statement, bishop? How do you feel about admitting the press to these sessions? The people have an inalienable right to know!"

I felt the eyes of the guardian lions sweep over me like blowtorches. Then, as it so often does under fire, inspiration born of fear-flooding adrenalin came to me. I drew myself up to my full height and thrusting forth the hard amplitude of my plastic paunch, I turned on the reporter.

"I'm going to give you an inalienable right to the mouth if you don't let go of me and clear out of here.